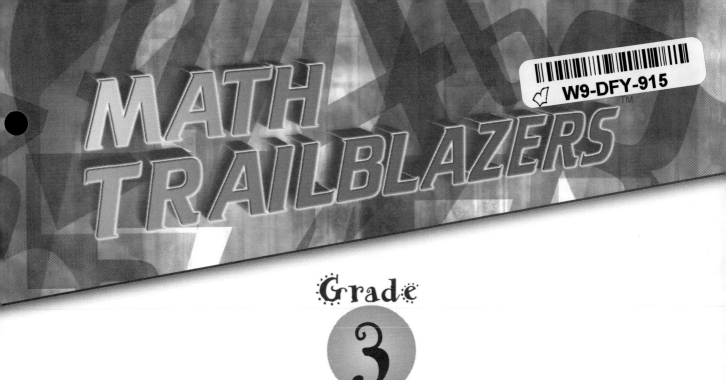

MATH TRAILBLAZERS

W9-DFY-915

Grade

3

Unit Resource Guide

Unit 20

Connections:
An Assessment Unit

SECOND EDITION

A Mathematical Journey Using Science and Language Arts

KENDALL/HUNT PUBLISHING COMPANY
4050 Westmark Drive   Dubuque, Iowa 52002
www.mathtrailblazers.com

A TIMS® Curriculum
University of Illinois at Chicago

UIC The University of Illinois at Chicago

The original edition was based on work supported by the National Science Foundation under grant No. MDR 9050226 and the University of Illinois at Chicago. Any opinions, findings, and conclusions or recommendations expressed in this publication are those of the author(s) and do not necessarily reflect the views of the granting agencies.

LETTER HOME

Connections: An Assessment Unit

Date: _____

Dear Family Member:

At this time of the year it is appropriate to look back and assess students' progress in mathematics. The activities in this last unit review and assess the concepts and skills we have worked on throughout the year. Two of the assessments are similar to the activities and labs they have done during the year and two are traditional tests. We also review and complete our portfolios.

In this unit, we investigate the relationship between the height of a tower of connecting cubes and its volume. Using this information, we should be able to tell the volume of a tower given its height or vice versa. As your son or daughter works on the lab and other activities, he or she is assessed not only for understanding of math content, but also for his or her abilities to solve problems and communicate results and solutions.

A connecting cube tower

As we review, you can help at home. For example:

- Encourage your child to bring home any of the math games we have played this year. The rules for most of the games are in the *Student Guide,* and many of the materials can be found at home.

- Ask your child to bring home his or her *Multiplication Facts I Know* chart and flash cards. Work with your child to review the multiplication facts. Knowledge of the multiplication facts will be assessed as part of this unit.

- Talk with your child about the experiments we have done this year. What were his or her favorites? Why? How were the labs like one another? How were they different?

- Review your child's portfolio together. Ask what he or she learned this year in math.

Thank you for working with me throughout the year.

Sincerely,

_____

UNIT OUTLINE

Connections: An Assessment Unit

Components Key: SG = Student Guide, DAB = Discovery Assignment Book, AB = Adventure Book, URG = Unit Resource Guide, and DPP = Daily Practice and Problems

	Sessions	Description	Supplies
LESSON 1 **Experiment Review** SG page 301 URG pages 15–22 DPP A–B	1	**ACTIVITY:** Students review the labs they have completed during the year.	• poster board or large sheet of paper • student portfolios
LESSON 2 **Tower Power** DAB pages 279–287 URG pages 23–31 DPP C–H	3	**ASSESSMENT LAB:** Students investigate the relationship between the height of a tower made from centimeter connecting cubes and its volume. They graph data and use the graph to make predictions about the heights and volumes of larger towers.	• centimeter connecting cubes • rulers • calculators
LESSON 3 **Becca's Towers** URG pages 32–36 DPP I–J	1	**ASSESSMENT ACTIVITY:** Students solve word problems about cube towers. They graph and interpret information from a data table. **ASSESSMENT PAGE:** *Becca's Towers*, Unit Resource Guide, page 35.	• calculators
LESSON 4 **Earning Money** URG pages 37–50 DPP K–N	2	**ASSESSMENT ACTIVITY:** Students work in groups to decide how to share five dollars equally among three people. They explain how the problem was solved. **ASSESSMENT PAGE:** *Earning Money*, Unit Resource Guide, page 46.	• calculators • scissors

	Sessions	Description	Supplies
LESSON 5 **End-of-Year Test** URG pages 51–58 DPP O–P	1–2	**ASSESSMENT ACTIVITY:** Students take a paper-and-pencil test of 14 short items which assesses concepts and skills studied throughout the year. **ASSESSMENT PAGES:** *End-of-Year Test,* Unit Resource Guide, pages 53–57.	• calculators • centimeter rulers

CONNECTIONS

A current list of connections is available at www.mathtrailblazers.com. Detailed information on software titles can be found in Section 13 of the Teacher Implementation Guide.

Software

■ *Building Perspective* develops spatial reasoning and visual thinking in three dimensions.

■ *Graphers* is a data graphing tool appropriate for young students.

■ *Kid Pix* allows students to create their own illustrations.

■ *Logo* is a drawing program that helps students develop spatial reasoning and an understanding of coordinates while making shapes.

■ *Mighty Math Calculating Crew* poses short answer questions about number operations, three-dimensional shapes, and money.

BACKGROUND

Connections: An Assessment Unit

This unit parallels the midyear assessment in Unit 10 *Numbers and Patterns: An Assessment Unit.* Both of these units provide a variety of assessment tasks that document your students' progress throughout the year. Since each of the activities in this unit is similar to an activity in Unit 10, students' work can be compared to their work on similar tasks at midyear. The results of these assessments, combined with information you have gathered through daily observations, will result in a comprehensive and balanced picture of their learning.

The unit begins with a review of the labs students have completed during the year. This review gives students an opportunity to reflect on the math and science concepts common to all of the experiments. The class discussion in this first lesson will set the stage for the final lab in Lesson 2 *Tower Power.* As students work on this experiment, you can assess their abilities to work on a task that extends over several days and requires the application of many

concepts and procedures. A shorter activity, *Earning Money,* can be used to assess students' abilities to apply their knowledge of the operations in a problem-solving situation and then to communicate their problem-solving strategies.

Two traditional tests are also part of this assessment menu. Since fluency with the multiplication facts is a goal of the third-grade curriculum, a test of all the multiplication facts is included in this final unit. The other test consists of short items designed to test important procedures, concepts, and skills studied in previous units.

The end of this unit is an appropriate time to review students' portfolios. Students can review and organize their portfolios in order to assess their own growth and to share their progress with their parents. For more information on portfolios, see the TIMS Tutor: *Portfolios* in the *Teacher Implementation Guide.*

Assessment Indicators

- Are students able to find the area of the base, volume, and height of a cube model?
- Can students collect, organize, graph, and analyze data?
- Can students make and interpret point graphs?
- Can students use patterns in data tables and graphs to make predictions and solve problems?
- Can students solve open-response problems and communicate solution strategies?
- Can students solve problems involving money?
- Do students demonstrate fluency with all the multiplication facts?

OBSERVATIONAL ASSESSMENT RECORD

(A1) Are students able to find the area of the base, volume, and height of a cube model?

(A2) Can students collect, organize, graph, and analyze data?

(A3) Can students make and interpret point graphs?

(A4) Can students use patterns in data tables and graphs to make predictions and solve problems?

(A5) Can students solve open-response problems and communicate solution strategies?

(A6) Can students solve problems involving money?

(A7) Do students demonstrate fluency with all the multiplication facts?

(A8) _____

Name	A1	A2	A3	A4	A5	A6	A7	A8	Comments
1.									
2.									
3.									
4.									
5.									
6.									
7.									
8.									
9.									
10.									
11.									
12.									
13.									

Name	A1	A2	A3	A4	A5	A6	A7	A8	Comments
14.									
15.									
16.									
17.									
18.									
19.									
20.									
21.									
22.									
23.									
24.									
25.									
26.									
27.									
28.									
29.									
30.									
31.									
32.									

Daily Practice and Problems

Connections: An Assessment Unit

Two Daily Practice and Problems (DPP) items are included for each class session listed in the Unit Outline. A Scope and Sequence Chart for the DPP can be found in the *Teacher Implementation Guide*.

A DPP Menu for Unit 20

Icons in the Teacher Notes column designate the subject matter of each DPP item. The first item for each class session is always a Bit and the second is either a Task or Challenge. Each item falls into one or more of the categories listed below. A menu of the DPP items for Unit 20 follows.

N Number Sense	**Computation**	**Time**	**Geometry**
A, C, F, J, L, M, O, P	F, I, L, M, O		N
Math Facts	**$ Money**	**Measurement**	**Data**
E, J, K		G, H, N	A–D

Practicing and Assessing the Multiplication Facts

By the end of third grade, students are expected to demonstrate fluency with the multiplication facts. In this unit students are assessed on all of the multiplication facts. Students should review the multiplication facts using the *Triangle Flash Cards* in preparation for the *Multiplication Facts Inventory Test* given in DPP item K. Encourage students to focus their review on the facts they have not circled on their *Multiplication Facts I Know* charts. Students can take home their flash cards for these facts or they can make new cards for these facts using the *Triangle Flash Card Masters* which follow the Home Practice in the *Discovery Assignment Book*.

Triangle Flash Cards for all the multiplication facts groups were distributed in Units 11–15 in the *Discovery Assignment Book*. They are also available in the Generic Section and the *Grade 3 Facts Resource Guide*.

For information on the distribution and study of the multiplication facts in Grade 3, see the Daily Practice and Problems Guide for Units 3 and 11. For a detailed explanation of our approach to learning and assessing the math facts in Grade 3 see the *Grade 3 Facts Resource Guide* and for information for Grades K–5, see the TIMS Tutor: *Math Facts* in the *Teacher Implementation Guide*.

Students may solve the items individually, in groups, or as a class. The items may also be assigned for homework.

Student Questions	Teacher Notes

A Averaging Data

Julie collected the following data at home. Find the median for each number of forks she measured.

N Number of Forks	L Length (in cm)			
	Trial 1	Trial 2	Trial 3	Median
1	15.8 cm	15.8 cm	15.8 cm	
2	31.2 cm	31.5 cm	31.2 cm	
4	62.5 cm	62.5 cm	62.8 cm	
8	125.0 cm	125.2 cm	124.8 cm	

TIMS Bit

The medians, from top to bottom, are 15.8 cm, 31.2 cm, 62.5 cm, and 125.0 cm.

B Graphing

Make a point graph using the data from TIMS Bit A on *Centimeter Graph Paper.* Do the points form a pattern?

TIMS Challenge

Distribute *Centimeter Graph Paper.* Remind students to label the axes. Have students decide on an appropriate scale. Good choices would be to count by ones on the horizontal axis and by tens on the vertical axis. Encourage students to draw a best-fit line.

Student Questions	Teacher Notes

C Joe Collects Data

Joe Smart filled in this data table. Moe Smart said to Joe, "You made four mistakes in your table." Can you help Joe find them?

C Con-tainer	V Volume (in cm)			
	Trial 1	Trial 2	Trial 3	Median
jar	490	520	486	490
cup	240	206	225	206
mug	284	272	290	272
glass	207	198	104	198

TIMS Bit

1. The units for volume should be cubic centimeters.

2. The median volume for the cup should be 225 cc.

3. The median for the mug should be 284 cc.

4. The value for the third trial in the last row is not reasonable. It is almost half the other two values. Joe should collect some more data.

D Graphing, Again

Make a bar graph using the corrected data from TIMS Bit C on *Centimeter Graph Paper.*

TIMS Challenge

Distribute *Centimeter Graph Paper.* Remind students to label their axes.

Have students decide on the scale. A good choice is to go by 25s on the vertical axis.

E Multiplication Facts

1. Which two multiplication facts were the hardest for you to learn?

2. Draw a picture and write a story for these facts. Label your picture with a number sentence.

3. Describe a strategy for each of these facts.

TIMS Bit

Discuss students' strategies. Remind students when the test on all the facts will be given. See DPP Bit K.

Framed Math

Find numbers that will make this sentence true. You can use fractions and decimals.

 $+$ △ $= 3$

Make a data table to show your answers.

Your table should have one column for

☐ and another column for △.

TIMS Task

Encourage the use of fractions and decimals. Some possible answers are:

☐	△
2	1
$2\frac{1}{2}$	$\frac{1}{2}$
$2\frac{2}{3}$	$\frac{1}{3}$

 Mill the Spill

Boo the Blob has a cousin named Mill the Spill. Find Mill's area.

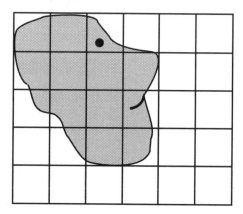

TIMS Bit

Approximately ten sq cm

H **Measure to the Nearest Cm**

1. Look around you for things of different lengths.

2. Use a cm ruler or tape measure to find their length to the nearest cm.

3. Make a data table showing things you measured and how long each is.

TIMS Task

Students need centimeter rulers to complete this task. You may need to review measuring to the nearest cm.

Student Questions	Teacher Notes

 Subtraction

Complete the following problems. Use pencil and paper or mental math to find the answers.

1. $\begin{array}{r} 6875 \\ -\ 4350 \\ \hline \end{array}$
2. $\begin{array}{r} 7015 \\ -\ 2550 \\ \hline \end{array}$
3. $\begin{array}{r} 896 \\ -\ 575 \\ \hline \end{array}$
4. $\begin{array}{r} 2003 \\ -\ 1497 \\ \hline \end{array}$

5. Explain a way to do Question 4 in your head.

TIMS Bit

1. 2525
2. 4465
3. 321
4. 506
5. Possible strategy: Students can count up from 1497 to 1500 (3), count up from 1500 to 2000 (500), and then 3 more to 2003. $3 + 500 + 3 = 506$.

 Mathhopper

If the following mathhoppers start at 0:

1. How many hops would it take for a +7 mathhopper to reach 56?

2. How many hops would it take for a +14 mathhopper to reach 56?

3. How many hops would it take for a +14 mathhopper to reach 560?

TIMS Task

Discuss the variety of strategies students use to solve these problems.

1. 8 hops

2. 4; Since the hop is twice as big as the +7 hop, it will take half as many hops. Skip count by 14 on the calculator or with paper and pencil.

3. 40; In Problem 2 we discovered that $14 \times 4 = 56$. Therefore, $14 \times 40 = 560$.

 Multiplication Facts Inventory Test

Have two pens or pencils of different colors ready. Use the first color when you begin the test. Your teacher will tell you when to switch pens and complete the remaining items with the other color pen or pencil.

TIMS Bit

The test can be found at the end of this set of DPP items, following item P. The test includes all the basic multiplication facts. After the test, students should update their *Multiplication Facts I Know* charts. Students should discuss strategies for figuring out or remembering any facts that they do not know well. They can record these strategies in their journals.

L Which Two Add Up?

| 39 | 276 | 149 | 57 |

1. Which two of these numbers should you add if you want an answer:

   A. over 400?

   B. less than 100?

   C. close to 200?

2. Which number when doubled will be close to 300?

Tell how you decided on your answers. Then, check your answers using base-ten shorthand or pencil and paper.

TIMS Task

1. A. 276 and 149

   B. 57 and 39

   C. 149 and 57 or 149 and 39

2. 149

M Another Mathhopper

A +17 mathhopper starts at 0 and takes 5 hops. Where does it land? Show how you would solve this problem without a calculator.

TIMS Bit

85; Students should discuss the strategies they used.

Some may think of 20 × 5 first and work from there. Others may use 17 × 10 and then cut their answer in half. Others may break the 17 into 10 and 7. Some might use addition.

N Dot the Blot

Boo's friend, Dot the Blot, has an area of 10 sq cm.

1. Draw Dot with all straight sides on *Centimeter Graph Paper*.

2. Draw Dot when she does not have straight sides.

TIMS Task

Distribute *Centimeter Graph Paper*. Ask students to fold the paper in half. They can draw one shape on the top half and one on the bottom.

1. Students do not have to draw a rectangle. Accept any shape with straight sides that has an area of 10 sq cm.

2. Remind them of Boo the Blob and that the area they draw will be approximate.

Play Digits: Sums

Draw boxes on your paper like these:

As your teacher or classmate reads the digits, place them in the boxes. Try to find the highest sum. Remember, each digit will be read only once.

The directions for Digits can be found in the activity *Digits Game* in Unit 6 Lesson 8 *More Adding and Subtracting*. Discuss the strategies students use to place the digits. How can you make the sum large? If an 8 is read first, where should you put it?

 Shaded Shapes

1. Is $\frac{1}{3}$ of the triangle shaded? Explain why or why not.

2. Is $\frac{1}{4}$ of the rectangle shaded? Explain why or why not.

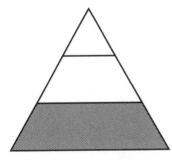

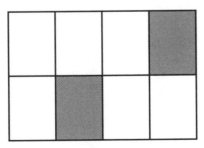

TIMS Task

1. No, the whole triangle is not divided into 3 equal parts.

2. Yes, $\frac{2}{8} = \frac{1}{4}$. If you move the shaded part that is in the corner so that it is above the other shaded part, it is easier to see $\frac{1}{4}$.

Name _____ Date _____

Multiplication Facts Inventory Test

Directions: You will need two pens or pencils of different colors. Use the first color when you begin the test. When your teacher tells you to switch pens, finish the test using the second color.

$\begin{array}{r}5\\ \times 5\\ \hline\end{array}$	$\begin{array}{r}4\\ \times 6\\ \hline\end{array}$	$\begin{array}{r}10\\ \times 7\\ \hline\end{array}$	$\begin{array}{r}5\\ \times 3\\ \hline\end{array}$	$\begin{array}{r}8\\ \times 7\\ \hline\end{array}$
$\begin{array}{r}2\\ \times 10\\ \hline\end{array}$	$\begin{array}{r}7\\ \times 7\\ \hline\end{array}$	$\begin{array}{r}10\\ \times 3\\ \hline\end{array}$	$\begin{array}{r}7\\ \times 4\\ \hline\end{array}$	$\begin{array}{r}6\\ \times 9\\ \hline\end{array}$
$\begin{array}{r}6\\ \times 6\\ \hline\end{array}$	$\begin{array}{r}9\\ \times 5\\ \hline\end{array}$	$\begin{array}{r}5\\ \times 2\\ \hline\end{array}$	$\begin{array}{r}4\\ \times 5\\ \hline\end{array}$	$\begin{array}{r}8\\ \times 8\\ \hline\end{array}$
$\begin{array}{r}6\\ \times 10\\ \hline\end{array}$	$\begin{array}{r}4\\ \times 2\\ \hline\end{array}$	$\begin{array}{r}3\\ \times 8\\ \hline\end{array}$	$\begin{array}{r}2\\ \times 7\\ \hline\end{array}$	$\begin{array}{r}10\\ \times 10\\ \hline\end{array}$
$\begin{array}{r}10\\ \times 9\\ \hline\end{array}$	$\begin{array}{r}4\\ \times 4\\ \hline\end{array}$	$\begin{array}{r}9\\ \times 9\\ \hline\end{array}$	$\begin{array}{r}8\\ \times 2\\ \hline\end{array}$	$\begin{array}{r}8\\ \times 4\\ \hline\end{array}$
$\begin{array}{r}6\\ \times 7\\ \hline\end{array}$	$\begin{array}{r}9\\ \times 4\\ \hline\end{array}$	$\begin{array}{r}10\\ \times 5\\ \hline\end{array}$	$\begin{array}{r}3\\ \times 3\\ \hline\end{array}$	$\begin{array}{r}7\\ \times 5\\ \hline\end{array}$
$\begin{array}{r}7\\ \times 9\\ \hline\end{array}$	$\begin{array}{r}8\\ \times 6\\ \hline\end{array}$	$\begin{array}{r}2\\ \times 3\\ \hline\end{array}$	$\begin{array}{r}3\\ \times 6\\ \hline\end{array}$	$\begin{array}{r}9\\ \times 3\\ \hline\end{array}$
$\begin{array}{r}10\\ \times 4\\ \hline\end{array}$	$\begin{array}{r}9\\ \times 8\\ \hline\end{array}$	$\begin{array}{r}6\\ \times 5\\ \hline\end{array}$	$\begin{array}{r}3\\ \times 4\\ \hline\end{array}$	$\begin{array}{r}7\\ \times 3\\ \hline\end{array}$
$\begin{array}{r}9\\ \times 2\\ \hline\end{array}$	$\begin{array}{r}5\\ \times 8\\ \hline\end{array}$	$\begin{array}{r}2\\ \times 2\\ \hline\end{array}$	$\begin{array}{r}10\\ \times 8\\ \hline\end{array}$	$\begin{array}{r}6\\ \times 2\\ \hline\end{array}$

LESSON GUIDE 1

Experiment Review

Estimated Class Sessions: 1

Students review the labs they worked on during the past year by recounting various elements of each lab: variables, number of trials, type of graph, problems solved, etc. The class discusses the experiments and describes differences and similarities.

Key Content

* Comparing and contrasting the following elements of experiments:

    variables

    measurement procedures

    number of trials

    types of graphs

    problems solved

Review Vocabulary

bar graph
point graph
trial
variable

Daily Practice and Problems: Bit for Lesson 1

A. Averaging Data (URG p. 8)

Julie collected the following data at home. Find the median for each number of forks she measured.

N Number of Forks	L Length (in cm)			
	Trial 1	Trial 2	Trial 3	Median
1	15.8 cm	15.8 cm	15.8 cm	
2	31.2 cm	31.5 cm	31.2 cm	
4	62.5 cm	62.5 cm	62.8 cm	
8	125.0 cm	125.2 cm	124.8 cm	

DPP Challenge is on page 20. Suggestions for using the DPPs are on page 20.

Materials List

Print Materials for Students

	Math Facts and Daily Practice and Problems	Activity	Homework
Student Books — Student Guide		*Experiment Review* Page 301	
Student Books — Discovery Assignment Book			Home Practice Part 1 Page 272 and *Triangle Flash Card Master* Pages 275–277
Teacher Resources — Facts Resource Guide	Use the *Triangle Flash Card Master* to create and review facts as needed.		
Teacher Resources — Unit Resource Guide	DPP Items A–B Page 8		

available on Teacher Resource CD

All Transparency Masters, Blackline Masters, and Assessment Blackline Masters in the Unit Resource Guide are on the Teacher Resource CD.

Supplies for Each Student

student portfolios

Materials for the Teacher

Stencilrama Graph Transparency Master (Unit Resource Guide) Page 22
transparency of a student's point graph from an experiment such as Unit 9 *Mass vs. Number*, optional
large sheet of paper or poster board for a class chart

Developing the Activity

The opening paragraph on the *Experiment Review* Activity Page provides a context for a class discussion reviewing the labs completed during the year. Professor Peabody is reminded of the assessment lab *Stencilrama* from Unit 10 as he uses a stencil to make a border around the top of his living room wall.

As part of the activity, the class will make a list of the labs they have completed throughout the year. Then, each of the labs can be assigned to a group of students for review. Start the review with a whole class discussion about *Stencilrama*. Analyze *Stencilrama* as an example by using **Question 2** from the *Experiment Review* Activity Page as a guide. The *Stencilrama Graph* Transparency Master has been provided to help you review the lab. **Question 3** then asks students to use the picture on the first page of the unit and their portfolios to make a list of the labs they remember working on during the year and to use **Question 2** to structure the analysis of the lab assigned to them.

Experiment Review

Professor Peabody was working at home redecorating his living room and hall. He used a stencil to make a border around the top of the living room wall. As he worked, he remembered a lab he worked on some months ago.

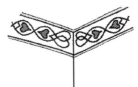

Discuss

1. Which lab does Professor Peabody remember?
2. Answer the following questions about that lab. You may use earlier units in the *Student Guide* or your portfolio to help you.
   A. What variables did you study in the lab?
   B. Did you have to keep any variables the same so that the experiment would be fair? If so, which ones?
   C. Did you measure anything? If so, what?
   D. How many trials did you do? If you did more than one trial, tell why.
   E. What kind of graph did you make, a point graph or a bar graph?
   F. What were the most important problems you solved using your data and your graph?
3. Look at the picture of Professor Peabody in his lab. This picture and the work in your portfolio can help your class make a list of the labs you completed. For each lab, answer each part of Question 2.

Experiment Review   SG · Grade 3 · Unit 20 · Lesson 1   301

Student Guide - Page 301

When all of the groups have completed their review, each group should make a report to the class. Organize the information from the reports on a class chart similar to the one in Figure 1. Note that sample responses to **Question 2** for *Stencilrama* are shown in the first column of the chart. A chart similar to this one will provide the data necessary for a class discussion comparing and contrasting labs.

Table of Sample Responses to Student Guide Questions Comparing Selected Experiments

Experiment's Elements	Unit 10 *Stencilrama*	Unit 1 *Kind of Bean*	Unit 5 *The Better "Picker Upper"*	Unit 9 *Mass vs. Number*	Unit 15 *Length vs. Number*	Unit 16 *Fill 'er Up!*
Main Variables	number of stencils, length of border	kind of bean, number of beans	type of paper towel, area of spot	number of objects, mass	number of objects, length of row	containers, volume
Fixed Variables	size and shape of stencils, the orientation of the stencil	size of scoop	number of drops, eye-dropper, position of towels (off desk)	size and shape of objects	size and shape of objects, the way the objects were placed	method of measuring
Anything Measured? (units)	length of border (in)	nothing measured—beans are counted	area of spots (sq cm)	mass of the objects (g)	length of row (cm)	volume (cc)
Number of Trials	1	1	3	1	Answers will vary; 3 is likely.	3
Type of Graph	point	bar	bar	point	point	bar
Problems (Answers will vary.)	predicted length of border for different numbers of stencils	predicted number of each kind of bean in a scoop	predicted number of drops of water to cover the whole towel	predicted mass of different numbers of objects	predicted length of rows of different numbers of objects	predicted number of small containers needed to fill the larger

Figure 1: *A sample experiment review class chart*

After all the groups have reported to the class and the information is displayed, continue the discussion with the following questions:

- *When doing an experiment, why do you need to keep some variables fixed?* To be able to look for patterns and make predictions involving the two main variables in an experiment, other variables must be held fixed. For example, to be able to make predictions about the length of a border made with a given number of stencils, the size, shape, and orientation of the stencil must be the same each time it is used. Students often think of holding variables in an experiment fixed as "keeping the experiment fair." In *The Better "Picker Upper,"* students were trying to find out which paper towel was the most absorbent by measuring the area of spots of water. To keep the experiment fair, it was necessary to keep the number of drops the same.

- *Why is it often a good idea to do more than one trial?* One reason scientists use multiple trials is to check on large errors in measurement and in controlling fixed variables. Error is often inevitable, so scientists use multiple trials so they can average out the error. However, if large errors in measurement are not likely, one trial may suffice. For example, one measurement was all that was needed to collect accurate data in *Stencilrama* because each time the stencil was used, the border grew exactly 3 inches.

- *How were point graphs used to make predictions?* If the points are close to a straight line, a line can be drawn which fits the points. The line can be used to make predictions. (Show a student's point graph from one of the experiments in which the student drew a line and made a prediction or you may use the *Stencilrama Graph* transparency as an example.)

- *Name two experiments that are alike. How are they alike? How are they different?* (You can ask this question more than once.) *Stencilrama* and *Mass vs. Number* are alike. In both experiments, students make predictions by measuring a small number of identical objects. Then they predicted a measurement for a larger number of objects using the data plotted on a point graph. In *Mass vs. Number,* students measured mass and in *Stencilrama,* students measured length. Students may also say that *The Better "Picker Upper"* is similar to *Fill 'er Up!* because they made bar graphs in both experiments. However, in *The Better "Picker Upper,"* they measured area and in *Fill 'er Up!,* they measured volume.

 Journal Prompt
Which two experiments did you like the best? Why? How are they alike? How are they different?

Daily Practice and Problems: Challenge for Lesson 1

B. Challenge: Graphing (URG p. 8)

Make a point graph using the data from TIMS Bit A on *Centimeter Graph Paper.* Do the points form a pattern?

Suggestions for Teaching the Lesson

Math Facts

Inform students when the test on all the multiplication facts will be given. This test is administered in DPP Bit K. Students can practice the facts using *Triangle Flash Cards,* concentrating their study on those facts they have not circled on their *Multiplication Facts I Know* charts. They can take their *Triangle Flash Cards* home or they can make new ones using the *Triangle Flash Card Masters* that follow the Home Practice in the *Discovery Assignment Book.* Flash cards for the multiplication facts groups are available in the Generic Section and the *Grade 3 Facts Resource Guide.*

Homework and Practice

- DPP Bit A asks students to find medians of data in a table and Challenge B asks them to graph the data. Students will need *Centimeter Graph Paper* for Challenge B.

- Home Practice Part 1 provides practice with multiplication, addition, and subtraction computation.

Answers for Part 1 of the Home Practice can be found in the Answer Key at the end of this lesson and at the end of this unit.

Name _____ Date _____

Unit 20: Home Practice

Part 1

1.	2.	3.	4.
70 $\times$ 9	877 + 549	51 $\times$ 8	551 − 435

5. 400 − 237 = _____   6. 719 + 281 = _____   7. 46 × 3 = _____

8. In the morning, Alex spends 25 minutes getting ready for school, an hour delivering papers, and 15 minutes walking to school. If Alex must be at school by 8:00, what time should he wake up?

Show your work. _____

_____

Part 2

1.	2.	3.	4.	5.	6.
893 − 5	893 − 95	893 − 495	645 + 6	645 + 86	645 + 986

7. Explain a strategy for solving Question 2 in your head.

8. A. At the movies, Roberto's mom spent $5.75 on two drinks and one bag of popcorn. If each drink costs $1.75, how much did the popcorn cost?

   B. If she paid with a ten-dollar bill, how much change should Roberto's mom get back?

272 DAB · Grade 3 · Unit 20   CONNECTIONS: AN ASSESSMENT UNIT

Copyright © Kendall/Hunt Publishing Company

Discovery Assignment Book - Page 272

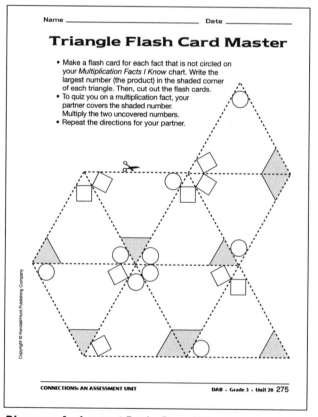

Discovery Assignment Book - Page 275

Math Facts and Daily Practice and Problems

DPP Bit A and Challenge B ask students to analyze and graph a set of data.

Developing the Activity

1. Students review the *Stencilrama* lab with the help of the *Experiment Review* Activity Page in the *Student Guide.*
2. Students review other labs completed throughout the year with the help of the *Experiment Review* Activity Page and their portfolios.
3. Students create a data table showing the components and attributes of completed labs.
4. Students compare and contrast labs to find similarities and differences.

Homework

1. Assign Home Practice Part 1.
2. Assign the multiplication facts as homework for students to review.

Notes:

Student Guide

Questions 1–3* (SG p. 301)

1. Stencilrama
2. **A.** number of stencils; length of border
   B. size and shape of stencils, the orientation of the stencil
   C. length of border in inches
   D. 1 trial
   E. point graph
   F. Answers may vary. We predicted the length of a border for different numbers of stencils.
3. See Figure 1 in the Lesson Guide.

Discovery Assignment Book

**Home Practice (DAB p. 272)

Part 1

Questions 1–8

1. 630
2. 1426
3. 408
4. 116
5. 163
6. 1000
7. 138
8. 6:20 A.M.

*Answers and/or discussion are included in the Lesson Guide.

**Answers for all the Home Practice in the *Discovery Assignment Book* are at the end of the unit.

Stencilrama Graph

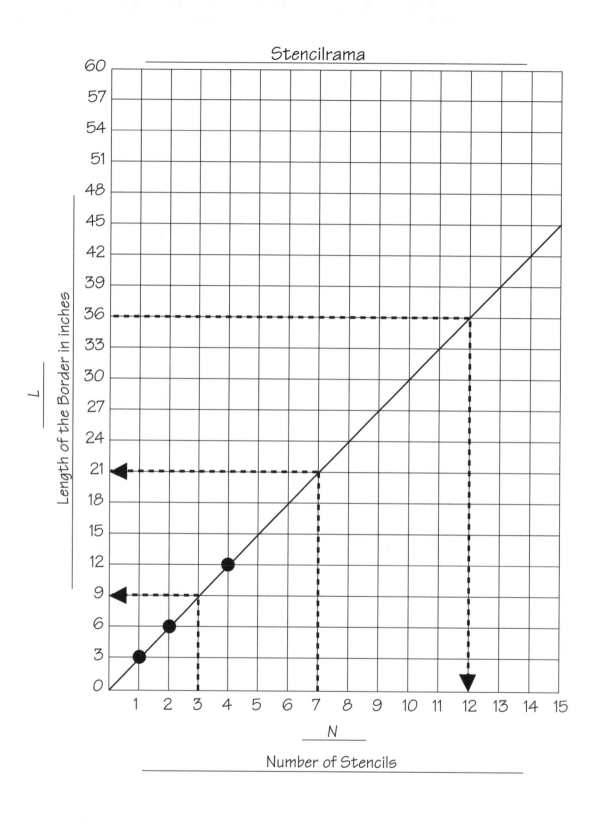

Stencilrama

Transparency Master

LESSON GUIDE

Tower Power

Estimated Class Sessions: 3

As students work on this lab, they assume the role of architects for Tiny TIMS Town. They work in groups to design an office tower for the town. While keeping the area of the floor plan fixed, students investigate the relationship between the heights and volumes of towers made from centimeter connecting cubes.

This lab is designed to allow children to make many of their own choices as they work in pairs or small groups. Students design a floor plan for their tower, choose values for the height of several towers, measure the volumes of these towers, organize their data, and graph the data as independently as possible. As the class works on the experiment, you will have an opportunity to assess their abilities to carry out an investigation and to use their data to make predictions and to solve problems.

Key Content

- Finding the area of the base, volume, and height of a cube model.
- Investigating the relationships between height, area, and volume.
- Collecting, organizing, graphing, and analyzing data.
- Using patterns in tables and graphs to make predictions and solve problems.
- Solving problems involving multiplication and division.
- Communicating solution strategies.

Daily Practice and Problems: Bits for Lesson 2

C. Joe Collects Data (URG p. 9)

Joe Smart filled in this data table. Moe Smart said to Joe, "You made four mistakes in your table." Can you help Joe find them?

C Container	V Volume (in cm)			
	Trial 1	Trial 2	Trial 3	Median
jar	490	520	486	490
cup	240	206	225	206
mug	284	272	290	272
glass	207	198	104	198

E. Multiplication Facts (URG p. 9)

1. Which two multiplication facts were the hardest for you to learn?

2. Draw a picture and write a story for these facts. Label your picture with a number sentence.

3. Describe a strategy for each of these facts.

G. Mill the Spill (URG p. 10)

Boo the Blob has a cousin named Mill the Spill. Find Mill's area.

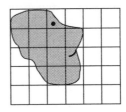

DPP Tasks and Challenge are on page 28. Suggestions for using the DPPs are on pages 28–29.

Materials List

	Math Facts and Daily Practice and Problems	Assessment Lab	Homework
Student Book — Discovery Assignment Book		*Tower Power* Pages 279–284	*Tower Power* Homework Section Pages 285–287
Teacher Resources — Facts Resource Guide	DPP Item 20E		
Teacher Resources — Unit Resource Guide	DPP Items C–H Pages 9–10		

⊙ available on Teacher Resource CD

All Transparency Masters, Blackline Masters, and Assessment Blackline Masters in the Unit Resource Guide are on the Teacher Resource CD.

Supplies for Each Student

40 centimeter connecting cubes per student group
250 additional centimeter connecting cubes available to the class for checking predictions
ruler
calculator

Materials for the Teacher

Observational Assessment Record (Unit Resource Guide, Pages 5–6 and Teacher Resource CD)

Developing the Lab

Read the introduction to the lab on the *Tower Power* Assessment Pages in the *Discovery Assignment Book* that describes the investigation and gives the student architects instructions for designing and building an office tower. The groups begin by choosing a floor plan with an area of 6 square centimeters. Each floor of the office tower will use the same floor plan.

Question 1A asks students about the important variables involved in the lab: Volume, Height, and Area of Floor Plan. *Questions 1B and 1C* ask which variables change and which stay the same. The height and volume vary from tower to tower. In order to investigate the relationship between height and volume, each group will have to keep the area of the floor plan the same (6 square centimeters) for each tower that they build. Following a discussion of *Question 1,* students draw their floor plans on grid paper that is provided on the *Tower Power* Assessment Pages.

After students design a floor plan, they build towers of three different heights, recording the height and volume for each tower in a data table. Student groups should work fairly independently on this lab. Students must choose the three heights for their towers and how to label the two-column data table that is provided. Students can also choose how they would like to work. They can either build one tower at a time, recording its data and then taking it apart, or they can build all three towers at once. Since the dimensions of the cubes are precise, one trial should give them accurate data. A blank data table is provided on the *Tower Power* Assessment Pages.

Discovery Assignment Book - Page 279

Discovery Assignment Book - Page 280

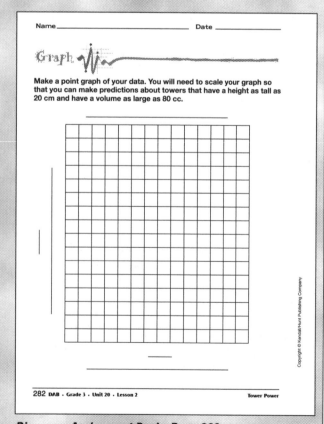

Discovery Assignment Book - Page 281

Name _____ **Date** _____

Record the height and volume of each tower. Label your data table. Don't forget to use the correct units.

Now, return to your drawing of the floor plan. On the same grid, show *one* of the following:

- a sketch of one of your towers
- a cube model plan of one of your towers
- the top, front, and right side views of one of your towers

Tower Power   DAB · Grade 3 · Unit 20 · Lesson 2   281

Name _____ **Date** _____

Graph

Make a point graph of your data. You will need to scale your graph so that you can make predictions about towers that have a height as tall as 20 cm and have a volume as large as 80 cc.

282 DAB · Grade 3 · Unit 20 · Lesson 2   Tower Power

Discovery Assignment Book - Page 282

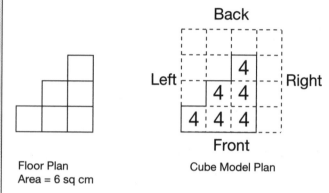

As students collect data and discuss the variables, be sure they are using the correct units for each variable: centimeters for height, cubic centimeters for volume, and square centimeters for area.

After the towers are built, students add a two-dimensional representation of one of their towers to their original drawing. They can either draw a sketch, make a cube model plan, or show the top, front, and right side views of one tower. Figure 2 shows a sample drawing of one tower's floor plan, which has an area of 6 square centimeters, and its cube model plan along with the corresponding data table.

Floor Plan
Area = 6 sq cm

Cube Model Plan

H	V
Height (in cm)	Volume (in cc)
2 cm	12 cc
4 cm	24 cc
6 cm	36 cc

Figure 2: *Sample data for a tower with a floor plan of 6 square centimeters*

When groups are ready to graph the data, they must decide on appropriate scales for each axis. The *Tower Power* Assessment Pages in the *Discovery Assignment Book* provide guidelines for choosing scales so that students will be able to use the graph to make predictions about the volume and height of larger towers. Figure 3 shows a sample graph (including answers for *Questions 3* and *4*). The horizontal axis is scaled by twos and the vertical axis is scaled by fives.

The sample graph in Figure 3 shows how to use the graph to make the predictions which are required for *Questions 3* and *4*. Students are also asked to check their predictions without using their graphs. Some students may use the cubes to build towers; others may use multiplication or division to solve the problem another way. Both methods are good choices.

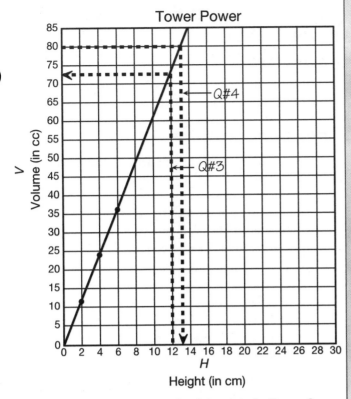

Tower Power

Figure 3: *Sample graph of the data in Figure 2*

A class discussion of the various methods can help students see the relationship between the concrete objects, the graph, and the operations of multiplication and division.

To solve **Question 4B,** students may skip count by sixes (the number of cubes in each floor) on a calculator 13 times to reach 78. There will be two cubes left over. If students use division to solve this problem, they will need to know how to interpret the remainder. Using a calculator $80 \div 6 = 13.333333$. Students should understand that the 3s to the right of the decimal point indicate a remainder, but will not make another whole floor.

Questions 5 and **6** ask the students to make predictions about very large towers without using their cubes or graphs to find the values. These questions provide an opportunity for students to solve problems using multiplication and division.

Journal Prompt
Which labs are like Tower Power? How are they alike? How are they different?

Discovery Assignment Book - Page 283

Discovery Assignment Book - Page 284

D. Challenge: Graphing, Again

(URG p. 9)

Make a bar graph using the corrected data from TIMS Bit C on *Centimeter Graph Paper.*

F. Task: Framed Math (URG p. 10)

Find numbers that will make this sentence true. You can use fractions and decimals.

$$\square + \triangle = 3$$

Make a data table to show your answers.

Your table should have one column for

$\square$ and another column for $\triangle$.

H. Task: Measure to the
Nearest Cm (URG p. 10)

1. Look around you for things of different lengths.

2. Use a cm ruler or tape measure to find their length to the nearest cm.

3. Make a data table showing things you measured and how long each is.

Suggestions for Teaching the Lesson

Math Facts

DPP Bit E discusses strategies for multiplication facts that students find difficult.

Homework and Practice

- DPP items C and D ask students to graph and analyze data. Task F asks students to complete a number sentence using fractions. Bit G asks students to estimate area by counting square centimeters and Task H provides practice with measuring to the nearest centimeter.

- Assign the Homework section in the *Discovery Assignment Book.* Students may solve the problems on these pages using interpolation, extrapolation, multiplication, or division. To answer *Question 8,* students can compare the volume of Toby's and Tysha's towers for any given height. For example, if Toby's tower has a height of ten centimeters, its volume is 50 cc *(Question 1).* Tysha's ten-story tower has a volume of 80 cc *(Question 4).* Therefore, the floor plan for Tysha's tower must have a larger area.

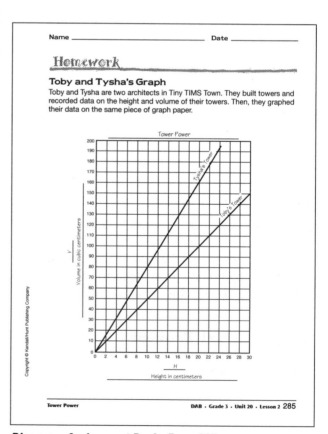

Discovery Assignment Book - Page 285

- To prepare for the *Multiplication Facts Inventory Test* in DPP Bit K, students should continue reviewing the multiplication facts using the flash cards.

Assessment

The lab provides opportunities to observe students' abilities to conduct the various parts of the laboratory investigation and work with data. Record your observations using the *Observational Assessment Record*. The following criteria can be used to assess student abilities in each phase of the lab:

- Drawing a picture
  1. Is the floor plan clearly illustrated?
  2. Have the students accurately made a two-dimensional representation of their tower?
- Collecting and recording data
  1. Is the data table well organized and clearly labeled?
  2. Are the correct units of measurement included?
  3. Are the measurements correct?
- Graphing data
  1. Is there a title?
  2. Are the axes scaled correctly and labeled clearly?
  3. Are the data points plotted accurately?
  4. Is the best-fit line drawn properly?
- Solving problems
  1. Are the strategies and solutions clearly communicated?
  2. Are the answers correct based on the data?

Name _____ Date _____

Use Toby and Tysha's graph to answer the following questions:

1. Toby built three towers with centimeter connecting cubes. He started to record his data. Fill in the data table completely.

Toby's Tower Power

H Height (in cm)	V Volume (in cc)
5 cm	
10 cm	
	100 cc

For Questions 2–8, find the answer and explain how you solved each problem.

2. What is the area of Toby's floor plan?

3. Toby wants to build a tower that is 30 cm tall. How many centimeter connecting cubes will he need?

4. Tysha built a tower 10 cm tall. What is the volume of her tower?

Tower Power

***Discovery Assignment Book* - Page 286**

Name _____ Date _____

5. Tysha built a tower that is 15 cm tall. What is the volume of this tower?

6. Tysha built a tower which has a volume of 160 cc. How tall was this tower? Write a number sentence for this problem.

7. If Tysha has 100 centimeter connecting cubes, how high can her tower be?

8. Whose tower floor plan is larger, Toby's or Tysha's? Explain how you know.

Tower Power

***Discovery Assignment Book* - Page 287**

AT A GLANCE

Math Facts and Daily Practice and Problems

DPP items C and D ask students to graph and analyze data. Bit E discusses multiplication facts strategies. Task F asks students to complete number sentences. Bit G asks students to estimate area and Task H provides practice with measuring length.

Developing the Lab

1. Read the introduction to the lab on the *Tower Power* Assessment Pages in the *Discovery Assignment Book*.
2. Students discuss the important variables of the investigation in **Question 1** on the *Tower Power* Assessment Pages.
3. Groups choose a floor plan with an area of 6 square centimeters.
4. Students draw their floor plans on grid paper.
5. Students use their floor plans to build towers of three different heights, label their data tables, and record the heights and volumes for each tower.
6. Students add a two-dimensional representation of one of their towers to their drawings.
7. Groups decide on appropriate scales for each axis and graph their data.
8. Students complete **Questions 2–6** on the *Tower Power* Assessment Pages.
9. Students use their graphs to make predictions for **Questions 3** and **4** and then check their predictions without using their graphs. Discuss the various methods they use.
10. In **Questions 5** and **6,** students make predictions about very large towers without using their cubes or graphs to find the values. Students may solve these problems using multiplication and division.

Homework

1. Assign the Homework section in the *Discovery Assignment Book*.
2. Remind students to study the multiplication facts using the *Triangle Flash Cards.*

Assessment

Review and assess the lab based on the criteria outlined in the Lesson Guide.

Notes:

Discovery Assignment Book

Tower Power (DAB pp. 279–284)

Questions 1–6*

See Figures 2 and 3 in the Lesson Guide for a sample picture, data table, and graph.

1. **A.** volume, height, and area of the floor

   B. height and volume

   C. area of floor

2. Answers will vary. The volume of each cube model is a multiple of 6. The volume is 6 times the height.

3. **A.** 72 cc; The extrapolation is shown on the graph in Figure 3 in the Lesson Guide.

   B. Strategies will vary. $6 \times 12 = 72$ cc; use more cubes if available and actually build the tower with height of 12 centimeters.

   C. Answers will vary. Yes, using the graph I predicted 72 cc which matches my answer in 3B. Also, I checked it by actually building the tower.

4. **A.** 13 centimeters tall; the volume would be 78 cc; The extrapolation is shown on the graph in Figure 3 in the Lesson Guide.

   B. *13 centimeters tall; $80 \div 6 = 13$ cm and 2 cubes left over; Using the calculator students may skip count by sixes (the number of cubes in each floor) 13 times to reach 78. Two cubes will be left over.

5. 660 cubes; Solution strategies will vary. $6 \times 110 = 660$ cubes

6. 100 centimeters tall; Strategies will vary. $600 \div 6 = 100$ cm

Homework (DAB pp. 286–287)

Questions 1–8

1.

H Height (in cm)	V Volume (in cc)
5 cm	25 cc
10 cm	50 cc
20 cm	100 cc

2. 5 square centimeters; Strategies will vary. Divide any of the volumes by their corresponding heights from the data table or use the graph.

3. 150 cubes; Use Toby and Tysha's graph and extrapolate from Toby's line. The volume is 150 cc.

4. 80 cc; Use Tysha's line on the graph. The volume is 80 cc.

5. 120 cc; Use the graph. The volume is 120. Divide the volume of any tower by its corresponding height and you will find that the area of each floor is 8 square centimeters. Then multiply the area of one floor by 15: $8 \times 15 = 120$ cc

6. 20 centimeters; Use the graph or division. $(160 \div 8 = 20)$

7. 12 centimeters; Use the graph or division. $(100 \div 8 = 12$ and 4 left over; 12 floors of 8 cc each and 4 cubes left over)

8. *The area of Tysha's floor plan is larger by 3 square centimeters.

---

*Answers and/or discussion are included in the Lesson Guide.

**Answers for all the Home Practice in the *Discovery Assignment Book* are at the end of the unit.

LESSON GUIDE

Becca's Towers

Estimated
Class
Sessions:
1

Students use Becca's tower data to make a line graph and solve problems using that data.

Key Content

- Making and interpreting point graphs.
- Using patterns in data tables and graphs to solve problems.
- Communicating solutions verbally and in writing.

Materials List

Print Materials for Students

		Math Facts and Daily Practice and Problems	Homework	Written Assessment
Student Book	Discovery Assignment Book		Home Practice Part 2 Page 272	
Teacher Resources	Facts Resource Guide	DPP Item 20J		
	Unit Resource Guide	DPP Items I–J Page 11		*Becca's Towers* Page 35, 1 per student
	Generic Section			*Centimeter Graph Paper,* 1 per student

available on Teacher Resource CD

All Transparency Masters, Blackline Masters, and Assessment Blackline Masters in the Unit Resource Guide are on the Teacher Resource CD.

Supplies for Each Student

calculator
centimeter connecting cubes, optional

Materials for the Teacher

Observational Assessment Record (Unit Resource Guide, Pages 5–6 and Teacher Resource CD)
Individual Assessment Record Sheet (Teacher Implementation Guide, Assessment section and
    Teacher Resource CD)

Developing the Activity

If *Becca's Towers* is used as assessment, students should complete the activity individually in class. Otherwise, students can work on these problems in pairs or in groups. Encourage students to explain how they solved the problems in *Questions 2–5.*

Suggestions for Teaching the Lesson

Math Facts

DPP Task J provides practice with jumps on a number line and division.

Homework and Practice

- DPP Bit I provides subtraction practice.
- Home Practice Part 2 provides practice with addition and subtraction.

Answers for Part 2 of the Home Practice can be found in the Answer Key at the end of this lesson and at the end of this unit.

Assessment

Use the *Observational Assessment Record* to record students' abilities to make and interpret point graphs.

Extension

Ask students to write their own problems that use Becca's data. Students should include some problems that use interpolation and others that use extrapolation. Have students exchange problems and share solutions.

Daily Practice and Problems: Task for Lesson 3

J. Task: Mathhopper (URG p. 11)

If the following mathhoppers start at 0:

1. How many hops would it take for a +7 mathhopper to reach 56?

2. How many hops would it take for a +14 mathhopper to reach 56?

3. How many hops would it take for a +14 mathhopper to reach 560?

Name_____ Date_____

Unit 20: Home Practice

Part 1

1.	2.	3.	4.
70 × 9	877 + 549	51 × 8	551 − 435

5. 400 − 237 = _____   6. 719 + 281 = _____   7. 46 × 3 = _____

8. In the morning, Alex spends 25 minutes getting ready for school, an hour delivering papers, and 15 minutes walking to school. If Alex must be at school by 8:00, what time should he wake up?

Show your work. _____

_____

Part 2

1.	2.	3.	4.	5.	6.
893 − 5	893 − 95	893 − 495	645 + 6	645 + 86	645 + 986

7. Explain a strategy for solving Question 2 in your head.

8. A. At the movies, Roberto's mom spent $5.75 on two drinks and one bag of popcorn. If each drink costs $1.75, how much did the popcorn cost?

   B. If she paid with a ten-dollar bill, how much change should Roberto's mom get back?

272 DAB · Grade 3 · Unit 20   CONNECTIONS: AN ASSESSMENT UNIT

Discovery Assignment Book - Page 272

AT A GLANCE

Math Facts and Daily Practice and Problems

DPP Bit I provides subtraction practice. Task J asks students to solve multiplication problems using skip counting.

Developing the Activity

Students complete the *Becca's Towers* Assessment Blackline Master.

Homework

Assign Home Practice Part 2.

Assessment

Use the *Observational Assessment Record* to record students' abilities to make and interpret a point graph. Transfer appropriate information from the Unit 20 *Observational Assessment Record* to students' *Individual Assessment Record Sheets*.

Notes:

Name _____   Date _____

Becca's Towers

Becca built towers out of centimeter connecting cubes. Then, she measured the height and the volume of each tower. Each tower had the same floor plan for each of its floors. Here is her data table.

Becca's Towers

H Height (in cm)	V Volume (in cc)
2 cm	6 cc
4 cm	12 cc
8 cm	24 cc

1. Make a point graph of the data on a separate sheet of graph paper. You will need to scale your graph so that you can make predictions about towers that are as tall as 30 cm and have a volume as large as 40 cc.

For Questions 2–5, be sure to explain how you solved each problem.

2. **A.** Use your graph to find the volume of a tower which is 12 cm tall and uses Becca's floor plan. On the graph, show how you solved the problem.

   B. Check your work by solving the problem another way. Use a number sentence in your explanation.

3. **A.** Becca is going to make a tower from 28 centimeter connecting cubes. Use your graph to find the height of the tallest tower which Becca can build using her floor plan. On the graph, show how you solved the problem.

   B. Check your work by solving the problem another way. Use a number sentence in your explanation.

4. Becca wants to build a tower that is 50 cm tall. How many centimeter connecting cubes will she need?

5. If Becca has 100 centimeter connecting cubes, how tall can a tower using her floor plan be?

Discovery Assignment Book

**Home Practice (DAB p. 272)

Part 2

Questions 1–8

1. 888
2. 798
3. 398
4. 651
5. 731
6. 1631
7. Possible strategy: $893 - 100 = 793$
   $793 + 5 = 798$
8. **A.** $2.25
   B. $4.25

Unit Resource Guide

Becca's Towers (URG p. 35)

Questions 1–5

1.

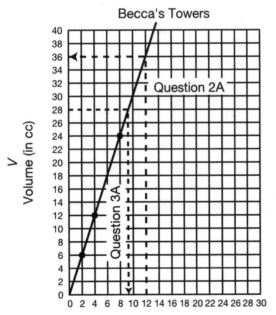

Becca's Towers

V
Volume (in cc)

H
Height (in cm)

2. **A.** 36 cc
   B. Solution strategies will vary. Divide any of the volumes by their corresponding height and you will find that the area of each floor is 3 sq cm. Then multiply the area of one floor by 12: $3 \times 12 = 36$ cc

3. **A.** 9 centimeters
   B. $28 \div 3 = 9$ cm and 1 cube left over; Students may skip count by 3 (number of cubes in each floor) to reach 27. There will be 1 cube left over.

4. 150 cc; $50 \times 3 = 150$ cc

5. 33 centimeters tall; $100 \div 3 = 33$ R1; Using a calculator, students may skip count by 3 (number of cubes in each floor) to reach 99. There will be 1 cube left over. If students divide 100 by 3 on the calculator, they will need to know how to interpret the remainder. Using a calculator shows $100 \div 3 = 33.333333$. Students should understand that the 3s to the right of the decimal point indicate a remainder, but will not make another whole floor.

---

*Answers and/or discussion are included in the Lesson Guide.

**Answers for all the Home Practice in the *Discovery Assignment Book* are at the end of the unit.

LESSON GUIDE

Earning Money

Estimated Class Sessions: 2

Students must decide how to divide five dollars equally among three people. Play money is made available to students to help them solve the problem. They are also asked to solve the problem using calculators. Students write explanations of how they solved the problem including a description of any tools used.

Key Content

- Solving open-response problems.
- Communicating problem-solving strategies.
- Solving problems involving multiplication and division.
- Interpreting remainders.
- Solving problems involving money.

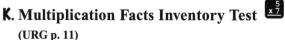

Daily Practice and Problems: Bits for Lesson 4

K. Multiplication Facts Inventory Test
(URG p. 11)

Have two pens or pencils of different colors ready. Use the first color when you begin the test. Your teacher will tell you when to switch pens and complete the remaining items with the other color pen or pencil.

M. Another Mathhopper (URG p. 12)

A +17 mathhopper starts at 0 and takes 5 hops. Where does it land? Show how you would solve this problem without a calculator.

DPP Tasks are on page 44. Suggestions for using the DPPs are on page 44.

Materials List

Print Materials for Students

		Math Facts and Daily Practice and Problems	Assessment Activity	Homework	Written Assessment
Student Books	**Student Guide**		Student Rubrics: *Knowing* Appendix A, *Solving* Appendix B, and *Telling* Appendix C and Inside Back Cover ◎		
	Discovery Assignment Book			Home Practice Parts 3 & 4 Page 273	
Teacher Resources	**Facts Resource Guide** ◎	DPP Item 20K			DPP Item 20K *Multiplication Facts Inventory Test*
	Unit Resource Guide	DPP Items K–N Pages 11–12 & 14 ◎	*Money Masters* Pages 58–60 from Unit 7 and *More Money Masters* Pages 47–49, 1 each per student group		DPP Item K *Multiplication Facts Inventory Test* Pages 11 & 14 ◎ and *Earning Money* Page 46, 1 per student

◎ *available on Teacher Resource CD*

All Transparency Masters, Blackline Masters, and Assessment Blackline Masters in the Unit Resource Guide are on the Teacher Resource CD.

Supplies for Each Student

calculator
scissors

Materials for the Teacher

TIMS Multidimensional Rubric (Teacher Implementation Guide, Assessment section and Teacher Resource CD)
Observational Assessment Record (Unit Resource Guide, Pages 5–6 and Teacher Resource CD)
Individual Assessment Record Sheet (Teacher Implementation Guide, Assessment section and Teacher Resource CD)

Developing the Activity

Before students begin working in their groups, the class should read the problem on the *Earning Money* Assessment Blackline Master. Students should understand that they have the option of using play money to help them divide the five dollars. They will be asked how a calculator can be used to solve the problem. The problem assesses students' abilities to solve an open-response problem involving division and to interpret any remainder.

Note that in the three samples of student work shown, each solution is quite different. All of the students had to interpret the remainder in some way, even though they did not necessarily use the division operation to find the answer. One group of students, whose work is not included, correctly solved the problem without having any money left over. They decided to buy bubble gum with the extra 2¢ and to divide the bubble gum into three pieces. Another group of students gave each student $1.50 and then said they would give the remaining 50¢ to the poor. Tell students that they must find the smallest possible remainder.

Since the money must be shared among three children, groups of three students work well for this activity. Once the groups have solved the problem, encourage students to write clear explanations of all strategies used. The groups can work together to write an explanation, or each student can write his or her own report.

To communicate your expectations to students, review with the class one or more of the student rubrics. Remind them to include a description of how they used calculators, play money, or other tools. If possible, give students an opportunity to revise their work based on your comments. For example, if a student only wrote about using play money, ask him or her to explain what happened when he or she tried a calculator. You may ask another student to include number sentences with his or her explanation.

In the following discussion, you will find three examples of student work with scores for each dimension of the *TIMS Multidimensional Rubric*. To assist you in scoring students' work, questions specific to this task have been developed. These questions are grouped within each dimension:

Solving

- Did students' strategies include the use of a calculator?
- Were students' strategies for dividing the money systematic and efficient?
- Did students organize their work?

- Did they look back at the problem and draw appropriate conclusions about their answers and the remainder?

Knowing

- Did students choose appropriate operations? Students' solutions may involve the following operations:

    1. *Multiplication, repeated subtraction,* or *repeated addition* as part of a guess-and-check strategy
    2. *Division* to divide the money into equal shares
    3. *Subtraction* to find the amount of money left over after each person has received a share

- Did students compute accurately?
- Did students use calculators effectively? If students used calculators to divide, were they able to interpret the decimal portion?
- Were students able to reconcile the solution they found using manipulatives with the solution they found using calculators?

Telling

- Did students clearly describe all of their strategies?
- Did students organize their work in a logical way?
- Did they use appropriate number sentences or other symbolic representations?
- Did they discuss any connections between decimals on a calculator, play money, and any real world situations?

Kim's Work

Didn't Work			
Daniel	Maria	Cora	
$1.70	$1.70	$1.70	O 10
$1.60	$1.60	$1.60	R O

Worked			
Daniel	Maria	Cora	
$1.65	$1.65	$1.65	5R
$1.66	$1.66	$1.66	2R

Kim's response the first day:

$1.66 R2 / $1.66 and 2¢ remaining to give to charity or something like that. I found my remainder by fidgeting around in my head, finding the answer and figuring out there's some remaining and I added $1.66 3 times and 2 remained.

$1.66 × 3 = $4.98
It gave us $4.98 and we knew $4.98 + 2 = $5.00 so, there was 2 remaining.

Teacher comments:

Since 1.70 × 3 = 5.10, you would have 10¢ too little—not enough to share equally. I don't understand the way you wrote your remainders in your table. Since 1.60 × 3 = 4.80, the remainder would be 20¢, not 0.

Mr. Fish

Kim did not correct her table.

Figure 4: *Kim's work*

Solving, 3

Kim used a guess-and-check strategy and organized her work in a table. She checked her guesses using a calculator and looked back at her final answer to make sure it was reasonable. Although her strategy was effective, it was not as efficient as it could have been.

Knowing, 3

Kim chose to use multiplication, addition, and subtraction. Most of her calculations are correct, but she did not always report the remainder correctly when she displayed her work in her data table. She also did not correct her table when her teacher pointed this

out. Even though she did not use division, she did indicate that there would be "2¢ remaining to give to charity or something like that."

Telling, 3

Kim reported on the use of addition, subtraction, and multiplication through the use of words, number sentences, and a data table. Each of her number sentences is clear and correct, and the data table is labeled so that we know which solutions she thinks "worked" and "didn't work." We are not entirely sure of her thinking, however, since she tells us she found her answer by "fidgeting around in my head . . . ."

Marco's Work

Marco's response the first day:

$3.65
× 3 kids
‾‾‾‾‾‾‾‾

three dollars and sixey five cenes times three kids, and five dollers minus one doller and foty five cenes egels fore dollers.

$5.00
− $1.45
‾‾‾‾‾‾‾
$4.00 ← not good

Teacher comments:

I'm still not clear from your explanation what you tried. Maybe you should try to explain to me. Did you use the money or the calculator? Try to finish today.

Ms. Ho

Marco's response the second day:

I didn't use the money, But I used a calculator.

```
75¢              165         $1.70
 75      $4.50   × 3         ×  3
 75    ×  3      ‾‾‾‾        ‾‾‾‾‾
‾‾‾‾   $1.50     4.95        $5.10
225
                1.67
        3.13    ×  3         1.69
        × 3     ‾‾‾‾         ×  3
  3     ‾‾‾‾    5.01         ‾‾‾‾
$1.10   3.39                 5.07
$1.10
+ $1.10         1.66
‾‾‾‾‾‾          ×   3
$3.30           ‾‾‾‾
                4.98
```

Figure 5: *Marco's work*

Solving, 2

Marco also used a guess-and-check strategy, but he made almost no attempt to organize his work in any way. Although his strategy was inefficient, he persisted until he found a solution.

Knowing, 2

Marco chose to use repeated addition and multiplication to check each guess. He never explicitly used subtraction to calculate the amount of money that would be left over, never identifying the remainder. This indicates that he did not completely understand all the mathematical concepts inherent in the problem.

Telling, 1

Marco wrote very little to explain his strategy or thinking. He showed all of his trials, but made no attempt to organize them. Since he did not identify which trial was successful, we are not even sure of his final answer.

Jayne's Work

Jayne's response the first day:

1.) Each person should get $1.66 and .2 left over. We got five dollars in change and we divided the money up between them. We got $1.66 for each person, and two cents left over.

2.) If you try on the calculator (5 ÷ 3) you would get 1.6666667. So I think it's much better to use play money or your head. The reason why you can't do it on the calculator is because the calculator will cut the coin up in half.

Teacher comments:

This is an excellent explanation! How can this problem help you solve other problems? Can you think of a way to find the remainder using your calculator?

Mrs. Vasquez

Jayne's response the second day:

1. You can check your answer by the calculator you can put $1.66 + $1.66 + $1.66 + $0.02 = $5.00.

2. This problem can help me solve other problems because it will help me divide money (if it involves money.)

3. A way to find how much is left $5.00 − $1.66 − $1.66 − $1.66 = $0.02.

Figure 6: *Jayne's work*

Solving, 4

Jayne used both the play money and a calculator to divide up the money efficiently. With a prompt from the teacher, she used two additional strategies to look back at her work and check her answer.

Knowing, 4

Jayne interpreted the problem as a division problem using both manipulatives and a calculator to perform the operation. All of her calculations were accurate. Although unsophisticated, her first interpretation of the decimal she got when she used the calculator was almost correct when she said, ". . . the calculator will cut the coin up in half." With a hint from her teacher, she was able to use the calculator to include the remainder in her calculations by using repeated addition and then adding in the remainder. She was also able to connect this addition sentence to the corresponding number sentence using repeated subtraction.

Telling, 3

Jayne's responses were very clear, and she correctly used number sentences or words to explain each of her strategies. She discussed the answers she got on the calculator along with the answer she got using manipulatives. However, we do not know how the group shared the play money. Did they trade the dollars for quarters and then the quarters for dimes, etc., or were they able to make the process more efficient in some way?

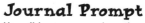 **Journal Prompt**

How did your group share the work on this problem? How do you feel about working with a group in math class?

Daily Practice and Problems:
Tasks for Lesson 4

L. Task: Which Two Add Up?

(URG p. 12)

39   276   149   57

1. Which two of these numbers should you add if you want an answer:

   A. over 400?

   B. less than 100?

   C. close to 200?

2. Which number when doubled will be close to 300?

Tell how you decided on your answers. Then, check your answers using base-ten shorthand or pencil and paper.

N. Task: Dot the Blot (URG p. 12)

Boo's friend, Dot the Blot, has an area of 10 sq cm.

1. Draw Dot with all straight sides on *Centimeter Graph Paper*.

2. Draw Dot when she does not have straight sides.

Suggestions for Teaching the Lesson

Homework and Practice

- DPP Task L provides practice estimating sums. Bit M asks students to solve a mathhopper problem. Task N reviews finding the area of shapes.

- Home Practice Part 3 provides practice with estimating and measuring. Home Practice Part 4 provides practice with ordering fractions and solving problems involving fractions.

Answers for Parts 3 and 4 of the Home Practice can be found in the Answer Key at the end of this lesson and at the end of this unit.

Assessment

DPP Bit K is the *Multiplication Facts Inventory Test.*

Name _____   Date _____

Part 3

1. Four 8-gram masses, three 5-gram masses, and three 1-gram masses balance an object. What is the mass of the object?

   _____

2. A. Name something at home that is about 15 inches long.

      _____

   B. Name something that is about 15 cm long. _____

   C. Name something that is about one meter long. _____

3. A graduated cylinder is filled with water, six marbles of the same size are added, and the level of the water rises to 54 cc. Each marble has a volume of 4 cc. How much water is in the cylinder?

Part 4

1. Which number is the largest? Which is smallest? Explain how you know. $\frac{13}{10}$ 2/10   0.9

   _____

2. You are going to have a party. 1/2 of your guests will be relatives, 1/4 will be classmates, and 1/4 will be neighbors. Plan how many people you will invite. Draw a picture on paper and label it clearly.

3. A. At midnight on New Year's Eve, 50% of the 70 balloons at a party were popped by the guests. How many balloons were popped?

      _____

   B. Five children divided the rest of the balloons. How many balloons did each child get? _____

CONNECTIONS: AN ASSESSMENT UNIT   **DAB · Grade 3 · Unit 20 273**

Discovery Assignment Book - Page 273

AT A GLANCE

Math Facts and Daily Practice and Problems

DPP Bit K is an inventory test on all the multiplication facts. Items L and M provide practice with addition and multiplication. Task N reviews area.

Developing the Activity

1. Review student rubrics. Advise students that their work for this activity will be scored using the rubrics.
2. Students read the problems on the *Earning Money* Assessment Blackline Master and use play money, calculators, and student rubrics to solve them.
3. Students revise their work based on teacher comments.

Homework

Assign Home Practice Parts 3 and 4.

Assessment

1. DPP Bit K is the *Multiplication Facts Inventory Test.*
2. Score student work using the *TIMS Multidimensional Rubric.*

Notes:

Earning Money

Daniel, Maria, and Cora earned five dollars baby-sitting for the Farleys. Mrs. Farley gave the three sitters one five-dollar bill.

1. If they share the money equally, how much should each baby-sitter get? Explain how you solved the problem.

2. What happens if you try to solve the problem on a calculator? Explain.

Write your solutions to Questions 1 and 2. Be sure to tell about all the ways you solved the problem.

Name _____ Date _____

More Money Masters

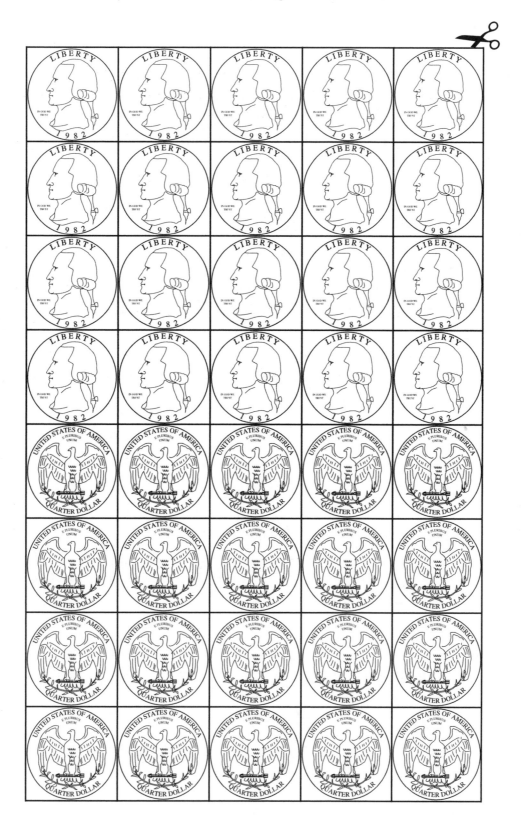

More Money Masters

Name _____ Date _____

More Money Masters

Discovery Assignment Book

**Home Practice (DAB p. 273)

Part 3

Questions 1–3

1. 50 grams

2. **A.** a newspaper, TV screen, placemat

   B. my mom's hand, a pencil, a stapler

   C. table top, height of a gym locker, the height of a chair

3. 30 cc

Part 4

Questions 1–3

1. $\frac{13}{10}$ is the largest; 2/10 is the smallest. $\frac{13}{10}$ means I have more than one whole. $\frac{10}{10}$ is one whole. 2/10 is part of a whole. 2/10 is the same as 0.2. 0.9 is the same as $\frac{9}{10}$. 0.9 is almost a whole.

2. Answers will vary. 20 people; 10 will be relatives, 5 will be classmates, and 5 will be neighbors.

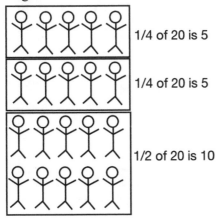

1/4 of 20 is 5

1/4 of 20 is 5

1/2 of 20 is 10

3. **A.** 35 balloons were popped.

   B. 7 balloons

Unit Resource Guide

Earning Money (URG p. 46)

Questions 1–2

See Figures 4–6 in the Lesson Guide for sample student work. *Students' responses are graded using the *TIMS Multidimensional Rubric*.

*Answers and/or discussion are included in the Lesson Guide.

**Answers for all the Home Practice in the *Discovery Assignment Book* are at the end of the unit.

LESSON GUIDE 5

End-of-Year Test

Estimated Class Sessions: 1–2

Students take a paper-and-pencil test consisting of 14 short items. Although these items test skills and concepts studied throughout the year, special emphasis is given to concepts addressed in the last ten units.

Key Content

*   Assessing concepts and skills developed throughout the year.

Daily Practice and Problems:
Bit for Lesson 5

O. Play Digits: Sums (URG p. 13)

Draw boxes on your paper like these:

$$\square \ \square \ \square$$
$$+ \ \square \ \square$$
$$\overline{}$$

As your teacher or classmate reads the digits, place them in the boxes. Try to find the highest sum. Remember, each digit will be read only once.

DPP Task is on page 52. Suggestions for using the DPPs are on page 52.

Materials List

Print Materials for Students

		Math Facts and Daily Practice and Problems	Written Assessment
Teacher Resource	Unit Resource Guide	DPP Items O–P Page 13 ⊙	*End-of-Year Test* Pages 53–57, 1 per student

⊙ available on Teacher Resource CD

All Transparency Masters, Blackline Masters, and Assessment Blackline Masters in the Unit Resource Guide are on the Teacher Resource CD.

Supplies for Each Student

centimeter ruler
calculator

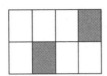
Developing the Activity

Students take the test individually. Although the test was designed to take one class session to complete, you may wish to give students more time. Students will need centimeter rulers and should have access to calculators for the second part of the test. The first page of the test consists of an addition problem, a subtraction problem, and a multiplication problem. These problems assess students' fluency with multi-digit addition, subtraction, and multiplication, so students should complete these items without the use of a calculator. Students should have the option of using a calculator for the remaining problems.

Emphasize the importance of following the directions for each item. Some of the items ask students to describe how they solved the problem. Encourage them to give full explanations of their problem-solving processes.

Suggestions for Teaching the Lesson

Homework and Practice

DPP item O develops addition number skills. Item P explores students' understanding of fraction concepts.

Assessment

Use the *End-of-Year Test* to assess students' skills and concepts studied throughout the year.

AT A GLANCE

Math Facts and Daily Practice and Problems

DPP Bit O provides addition practice. Task P reviews fraction concepts.

Developing the Activity

1. Students complete the first page of the test without a calculator.
2. Students complete the rest of the test with centimeter rulers and calculators.

Notes:

End-of-Year Test

Part 1

You *may not* use your calculator on this page. You *may* use your calculator on the rest of the pages. Show how you solve each problem.

I. **A.** In one month, Mrs. Miranda's class read 7240 pages. During the same month, Mr. Carlton's class read 6965 pages. How many pages did both classes read?

B. How many more pages did Mrs. Miranda's class read than Mr. Carlton's class?

2. Professor Peabody has to tile a hall. He will need five rows of tile, with 27 tiles in each row. How many tiles will he need?

Name _____   Date _____

Part 2

For the rest of the test, you may use any of the tools you have used in class. For example, you may wish to use a ruler or a calculator.

3. Here is a shape to measure. Measure lengths to the nearest tenth of a centimeter.

   A. What is its area? _____

   B. What is its perimeter? _____

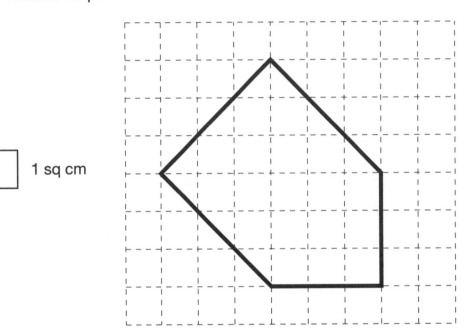

   1 sq cm

   C. How many sides does the shape have? _____

   D. How many vertices (corners) does it have? _____

   E. How many right angles does it have? _____

4. Daniel made 32 ounces of lemonade. How many 6-ounce cups could he fill? How much would be left over? Show your work.

Assessment Blackline Master

5. Tell the time that is on the clock. _____

6. **A.** Write the coordinates of the triangle and square on the data table.

   B. Draw the circle at the correct point on the map.

Object	Right	Front
■		
▲		
●	6	5

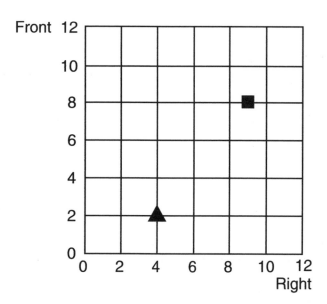

7. Show the number 2469 in base-ten shorthand.

8. **A.** Write $\frac{5}{10}$ as a decimal. _____

   B. Write 0.7 as a common fraction. _____

   C. Shade 0.5 of this picture.

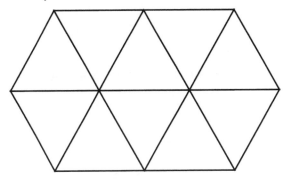

9. If this 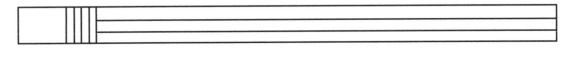 is 1/3, then draw one whole.

10. Measure the length of the pencil to the nearest tenth of a centimeter.

   Length _____

11. Write three fractions that are equal to 1/2.

12. Which is bigger, 1.2 or $\frac{1}{2}$? Or are they equal? Tell how you know.

13. Dora put some marbles in one pan of a two-pan balance. She balanced the pans with three 10-gram masses, seven 5-gram masses, and two 1-gram masses. What is the marbles' mass? Explain how you found your answer.

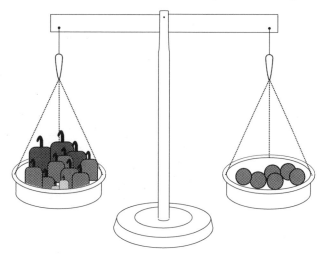

14. Peter put a rock in the water in the graduated cylinder shown below.

What was the volume of the rock? _____

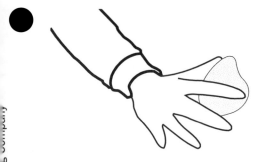

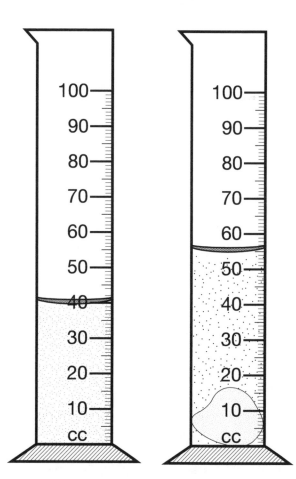

Unit Resource Guide

End-of-Year Test (URG pp. 53–57)

Questions 1–14

1. **A.** 14,205 pages

   B. 275 pages

2. 135 tiles

3. **A.** $22\frac{1}{2}$ square centimeters

   B. Measurements of each segment may be off by 0.1 cm. Accept any answer between 18.2–19.2 centimeters.

   C. 5 sides

   D. 5 vertices

   E. 3 right angles

4. 5 cups and 2 ounces remaining

5. 7:25

6. **A.** square: 9 right, 8 front
      triangle: 4 right, 2 front

   B. The dot should be placed at 6 right, 5 front.

7.

8. **A.** 0.5

   B. $\frac{7}{10}$

   C. Any five triangles can be shaded.

9. Shapes will vary. Here are three examples.

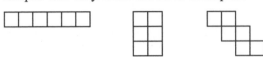

10. 14.7–14.9 centimeters

11. Answers will vary. Possible answers are: 2/4, 7/14, and 50/100

12. 1.2 is larger; 1.2 is larger than one whole. 1/2 is part of a whole or less than one whole.

13. 67 grams; Explanations will vary. 3×10 grams $+ 7 \times 5$ grams $+ 2 \times 1$ gram $= 67$ grams

14. 15 cc; 55 cc $-$ 40 cc $=$ 15 cc

*Answers and/or discussion are included in the Lesson Guide.

**Answers for all the Home Practice in the *Discovery Assignment Book* are at the end of the unit.

Discovery Assignment Book

Part 1

Questions 1–8 (DAB p. 272)

1. 630
2. 1426
3. 408
4. 116
5. 163
6. 1000
7. 138
8. 6:20 A.M.

Part 2

Questions 1–8 (DAB p. 272)

1. 888
2. 798
3. 398
4. 651
5. 731
6. 1631
7. Possible strategy: $893 - 100 = 793$
   $793 + 5 = 798$
8. **A.** $2.25
   B. $4.25

Part 3

Questions 1–3 (DAB p. 273)

1. 50 grams
2. **A.** a newspaper, TV screen, placemat
   B. my mom's hand, a pencil, a stapler
   C. table top, height of a gym locker, the height of a chair
3. 30 cc

Part 4

Questions 1–3 (DAB p. 273)

1. $\frac{13}{10}$ is the largest; 2/10 is the smallest. $\frac{13}{10}$ means I have more than one whole. $\frac{10}{10}$ is one whole. 2/10 is part of a whole. 2/10 is the same as 0.2. 0.9 is the same as $\frac{9}{10}$. 0.9 is almost a whole.

2. Answers will vary. 20 people; 10 will be relatives, 5 will be classmates, and 5 will be neighbors.

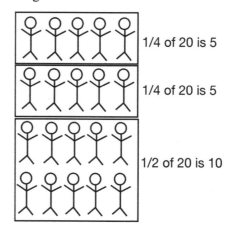

1/4 of 20 is 5

1/4 of 20 is 5

1/2 of 20 is 10

3. **A.** 35 balloons were popped.
   B. 7 balloons

---

*Answers and/or discussion are included in the Lesson Guide.